The App
Poems for

Presented to
Timothy SEERS

on leaving the school in July 2003

Signed: _____ Headteacher

The Isis C. E. Middle School

The Apple-Raid

Poems for Year 6

Chosen by Pie Corbett

MACMILLAN CHILDREN'S BOOKS

First published 2001
by Macmillan Children's Books
a division of Pan Macmillan Limited
20 New Wharf Road, London N1 9RR
Basingstoke and Oxford
www.panmacmillan.com

Associated companies throughout the world

ISBN 0 330 48291 2

1 3 5 7 9 8 6 4 2

A CIP catalogue record for this book is available from the British Library.

Printed by Mackays of Chatham plc, Chatham, Kent.

Contents

Introduction   1
The Oldest Girl in the World   *Carol Ann Duffy*   5
Pomegranates Do Not Feel Pain   *Helen Dunmore*   8
Peach   *Rose Rauter*   9
The Apple's Song   *Edwin Morgan*   10
Not Only   *Brian Patten*   11
Hedgehog Hiding at Harvest in Hills
     Above Monmouth   *Helen Dunmore*   12
What the Mountain Knows   *Brian Patten*   13
Thaw   *Edward Thomas*   14
Snow   *Edward Thomas*   15
December Moon   *Brian Moses*   16
Take Two   *Pie Corbett*   17
City Jungle   *Pie Corbett*   18
Goodnight Stroud   *Pie Corbett*   19
In a Station of the Metro   *Ezra Pound*   20
New Year Exhilaration   *Ted Hughes*   21
The Red Wheelbarrow   *William Carlos Williams*   22
The Birth of the Foal   *Ferenc Juhász*   23
Sheep-dreams   *Lawrence Sail*   25
Owl on the Nursery Window Sill
     Katherine Gallagher   26
Tree-Planting   *Katherine Gallagher*   27
From Fourteen Ways of
     Touching the Peter   *George MacBeth*   28
Lizards   *Darren Stanley*   31
The Mystery of the Ant   *George Szirtes*   32
The Bee's Knees   *George Szirtes*   33
My Mother Saw a Dancing Bear   *Charles Causley*   34
The Green Bear   *Richard Edwards*   35
There Isn't a Monkey in the Attic   *Richard Edwards*   37

For Francesca   *Helen Dunmore*   39
Small Dawn Song   *Philip Gross*   40
Snowy Benches   *Aileen Fisher*   41
My Brother   *Bobbi Katz*   42
Leave Me Alone   *Felice Holman*   43
Alone on the Playground   *Wes Magee*   44
Where Nobody Lives   *Dave Ward*   46
The Window's Eyes   *George Szirtes*   47
Give Me Back My Rags   *Vasko Popa*   48
The Bully Asleep   *John Walsh*   49
The Guide   *Gerard Benson*   51
Witches' Chant   *William Shakespeare*   53
Stufferation   *Adrian Mitchell*   55
Cock-A-Roodle Dock   *David Greygoose*   58
Once Upon a Time Machine   *Dave Ward*   60
Jabberwocky   *Lewis Carroll*   61
Shoem   *Liz Brownlee*   63
Unscrambled Egg   *Tony Charles*   64
A Bad Princess   *Carol Ann Duffy*   65
Three   *Carol Ann Duffy*   67
Extracts from The Tempest   *William Shakespeare*   69
Wolf in My Pocket   *Helen Dunmore*   72
It's Dark in Here   *Shel Silverstein*   73
This is Just to Say   *William Carlos Williams*   74
Variations on a Theme   *Kenneth Koch*   75
Clementine   *Anonymous*   76
In a cavern, in a canyon   *Paul Dehn*   77
Sing a Song of Sixpence   *Anonymous*   78
Sing a Song of Subways   *Eve Merriam*   79
Instructions for Giants   *John Rice*   80
The Sleepy Giant   *Charles Edward Carryl*   81

One of the Difficulties of
   Writing a Poem   *Brian Patten*   82
The Computer's First
   Chirstmas Card   *Edwin Morgan*   83
Snake   *Valerie Bloom*   85
A Fistful of Pacifists   *David Kitchen*   86
Kennings Cat   *Sandy Brownjohn*   87
Winter Haikus   *John Kitching*   88
The Limerick Orchestra   *John Kitching*   89
Palindrome   *Lawrence Sail*   90
Riddle   *Kevin Crossley-Holland*   91
Riddles   *John Cotton*   92
Old English Riddle   *Gerard Benson*   93
Goodnight   *Pamela Gillilan*   94
Frostbringer   *Catherine Fisher*   95
The Apple-Raid   *Vernon Scannell*   97

Introduction

An anthology can be like a family, or a gathering of old friends. I'd like you to meet some of mine. Many of these poems I have known for a long time. Coming back to them I realize that they are so strong that the passing of time seems to have enriched their meaning. But there are also some new additions – fresh sparks that caught my eye like sudden gleams of sunlight. Sharply cut diamonds that reflect some facet of who we are.

I suppose I am lucky – my poetry family is quite large. So, how was I to choose the 60 or so poems for this book? Well, in a way it was easy enough. At first hundreds of old friends jostled for attention. But I wanted poems that I had shared with children on many occasions. Poems that I knew would appeal, would interest and fascinate. Poems that would resonate in the mind long after their reading. So they had to be strong poems.

I wanted to bring together poems that were related – so that they would sometimes speak to each other in their own language, echoing back and forth across the pages. I wanted to have poems that I knew would not always be too easily grasped. Poems that might need thinking about. Not everything in life is easy to understand and sometimes the most mysterious are the most amazing – I could never fathom how a magnet works, but they have always fascinated me. Just because things are difficult to understand does not mean they cannot intrigue, or be beautiful. Poems are not like simple sums – these old friends cannot always be tied down easily, but meet them, greet them and enjoy them.

And I wanted poems that could act as a kick-start to

writing. Many of these poems are old standbys – faithful retainers, who have helped thousands of children find poetry within themselves, a self-confidence to put a word in, their word. Many of these poems have been the catalyst to children's own writing – and I have been lucky enough to witness some remarkable poems being written, in moments when something of our common genius poked its nose round the corner to surprise us all. So, I needed poems that I knew could strengthen imagination, release invention and ignite writing. If you like, this collection is a toolbox for creative teachers, readers and writers.

Finally, I imagined myself with a class of Year 6 children and thought about what poetry equipment we might need to take us through the journey of a year together. Poems that we could lean upon, poems that would surprise us, poems of many shades and moods. Poems that did not patronize. Poems that might light up a lifetime.

I took account of the national literacy strategy. So, there are poems by long-established and significant poets, including Shakespeare and poets from other cultures. There are poems written in a range of forms including nonsense verse as well as poems that manipulate words for their sounds, connotations and layers of meaning. There are poems that use figurative language such as simile, metaphor and personification as well as poems that are multi-layered and challenging. There are poems that address the same theme, and are linked or form part of a sequence. All this is included – but, to be honest, whilst this helped to sharpen the choice, it never hindered. And besides, I wanted poems so strong that they would speak to others – those interested in writing in secondary

2

schools and beyond. Not just poems written for an eleven year old. But poems that had demanded to be written.

So, step inside – meet this gathering of old friends and relations. Give them some time and you will get to know them well – and, maybe, make friends for life. You may even be tempted to create a few – take a step out of the darkness of yourself. Step into sunlight. It feels good to make new friends, to create something new.

Pie Corbett
March 2001

The Oldest Girl in the World

Children, I remember how I could hear
with my soft young ears
the tiny sounds of the air –
tinkles and chimes
like minuscule bells
ringing continually there;
clinks and chinks
like glasses of sparky gooseberry wine,
jolly and glinting and raised in the air.
Yes, I could hear like a bat. And how!
Can't hear a sniff of it now.

Truly, believe me, I could all the time see
every insect that crawled in a bush,
every bird that hid in a tree,
individually.
If I wanted to catch a caterpillar
to keep as a pet in a box
I had only to watch a cabbage
and there it would be
crawling bendy and green towards me.
Yes, I could see with the eyes of a cat. Miaow!
Can't see a sniff of it now.

And my sense of taste was second to none,
By God, the amount I knew with my tongue!
The shrewd taste of a walnut's brain.
The taste of a train from a bridge.
Of a kiss. Of air chewy with midge.
Of fudge from a factory two miles away
from the house where I lived.
I'd stick out my tongue
to savour the sky in a droplet of rain.
Yes, I could taste like the fang of a snake. Wow!
Can't taste a sniff of it now.

On the scent, what couldn't I smell
with my delicate nose, my nostrils of pearl?
I could smell the world!
Snow. Soot. Soil.
Satsumas snug in their Christmas sock.
The ink of a pen.
The stink of an elephant's skin.
The blue broth of a swimming-pool. Dive in!
The showbizzy gasp of the wind.
Yes, I could smell like a copper's dog. Bow-wow!
Can't smell a sniff of it now.

As for my sense of touch
it was too much!
The cold of a snowball
felt through the vanishing heat of a mitt.
A peach like an apple wearing a vest.
The empty dish of a bird's nest.
A hot chestnut
branding the palm at the heart of the fist.
The stab of the thorn on the rose. Long grass, its itch.
Yes, I could feel with the sensitive hand of a ghost.
   Whooo!
Can't feel a sniff of it now.

Can't see a
Can't hear a
Can't taste a
Can't smell a
Can't feel a bit of it whiff of it sniff of it.
Can't get a sniff of it now.

Carol Ann Duffy

7

Pomegranates Do Not Feel Pain

Fasten your face on to its flesh
and suck each bead through your teeth,

dig out the pips with a tarnished teaspoon
while you sit on top of the washing machine,

squeeze half-moons on a lemon-squeezer
(make sure you're wearing a white T-shirt)

or stab your pomegranate with a whelk pin –
pomegrantes do not feel pain.

Helen Dunmore

Peach

Touch it to your cheek and it's soft
as a velvet newborn mouse
who has to strive
to be alive.

Bite in. Runny
honey
blooms on your tongue –
as if you've bitten open
a whole hive.

Rose Rauter

The Apple's Song

Tap me with your finger,
rub me with your sleeve,
hold me, sniff me, peel me,
curling round and round
till I burst out white and cold
from my tight red coat
and tingle in your palm
as if I'd melt and breathe
a living pomander
waiting for the minute
of joy when you lift me
to your mouth and crush me
and in taste and fragrance
I race through your head
in my dizzy dissolve.

I sit in the bowl
in my cool corner
and watch you as you pass
smoothing your apron.
Are you thirsty yet?
My eyes are shining.

Edwin Morgan

Not Only

Not only the leaf shivering with delight
No,
Not only the morning grass shrugging off the weight of
     frost
No,
Not only the wings of the crane fly consumed by fire
No,
Not only the steam rising from the horse's back
No,
Not only the sound of the sunflower roaring
No,
Not only the golden spider spinning
No,
Not only the cathedral window deep inside the raindrop
No,
Not only the door opening at the back of the clouds
No,
Not only flakes of light settling like snow
No,
Not only the sky as blue and smooth as an egg
No,
Not only these things.

Brian Patten

Hedgehog Hiding at Harvest in Hills Above Monmouth

Where you hide
    moon-striped grass ripples like tiger skin
where you hide
    the dry ditch rustles with crickets

where you hide
    the electricity pylon saws and sighs
    and the combine harvester's headlight
    pierces the hedges

where you hide
    in your ball of silence
    your snorts muffled
    your squeaks and scuffles
    gone dumb

a foggy moon sails over your head,
the stars are nipped in the bud

where you hide
    you hear the white-faced owl hunting
    you count the teeth of the fox.

Helen Dunmore

What the Mountain Knows

It is the hare's breath melting the snow

causes the avalanche.

Brian Patten

Thaw

Over the land freckled with snow half-thawed

The speculating rooks at their nests cawed

And saw from elm-tops, delicate as flower of grass,

What we below could not see. Winter pass.

Edward Thomas

Snow

In the gloom of whiteness,
In the great silence of snow,
A child was sighing
And bitterly saying: 'Oh,
They have killed a white bird up there on her nest,
The down is fluttering from her breast!'
And still it fell through that dusky brightness
On the child crying for the bird of the snow.

Edward Thomas

December Moon

The moon has come out too soon,
it's still the middle of the afternoon
and the day shows no sign of darkness.

What is the moon doing,
sneaking into the sky when it's light?

What is the moon playing at?
Couldn't it sleep?
Has its alarm clock run too soon?

Do we see the moon this early
in June or September?

Or does December bring a special moon,
a let's-get-these-nights-over-soon moon,
a can't-wait-for-Christmas-to-come moon?

Brian Moses

Take Two

A bruise of wind
fists the street;
a knuckle of rain
punches south.

The shutters bark
back and the moon
coughs discretely.

The fog busies itself
up some clipped alleyway.

Night nibbles dawn.

The stars lose control.

Pie Corbett

City Jungle

Rain splinters town.

Lizard cars cruise by;
their radiators grin.

Thin headlights stare –
shop doorways keep
their mouths shut.

At the roadside
hunched houses cough.

Newspapers shuffle by,
hands in their pockets.
The gutter gargles.

A motorbike snarls;
Dustbins flinch.

Streetlights bare
their yellow teeth.
The motorway's cat-black tongue
lashes across
the glistening back
of the tarmac night.

Pie Corbett

Goodnight Stroud

The Clock Tower glowers.
Its hands fidget
towards dawn.

Dark streets yawn.
　　It's late –
the streets wait –
　　restless as rain.

Trains idle up sidelines;
a cyclist sidles by.

Black taxis scuttle
down back alleys.

A bright bus blunders
up the High Street.

The Belisha Beacon blinks.

Parked cars huddle,
like wet toads;
the night thinks
that the stars
are sending morse-code.

Pie Corbett

In a Station of the Metro

The apparition of these faces in a crowd;

Petals on a wet, black bough.

Ezra Pound

New Year Exhilaration

On the third day
Finds its proper weather. Pressure
Climbing and the hard blue sky
Scoured by gales. The world's being
Swept clean. Twigs that can't cling
Go flying, last leaves ripped off
Bowl along roads like daring mice. Imagine
The new moon hightide sea under this
Rolling of air-weights. Exhilaration
Lashes everything. Windows flash,
White houses dazzle, fields glow red.
Seas pour in over the land, invisible maelstroms
Set the house-joints creaking. Every twig-end
Writes its circles and the earth
Is massaged with roots. The powers of the hills
Hold their bright faces in the wind-shine.
The hills are being honed. The river
Thunders like a factory, its weirs
Are tremendous engines. People
Walk precariously, the whole landscape
Is imperilled, like a tarpaulin
With the wind under it. 'It nearly
Blew me up the chymbley!' And a laugh
Blows away like a hat.

(3 January 1975)
Ted Hughes

The Red Wheelbarrow

so much depends
upon

a red wheel
barrow

glazed with rain
water

beside the white
chickens

William Carlos Williams

The Birth of the Foal

As May was opening the rosebuds,
elder and lilac beginning to bloom,
it was time for the mare to foal.
She'd rest herself, or hobble lazily

after the boy who sang as he led her
to pasture, wading through the meadow flowers.
They wandered back at dusk, bone-tired,
the moon perched on a blue shoulder of sky.

Then the mare lay down,
sweating and trembling, on her straw in the stable.
The drowsy, heavy-bellied cows
surrounded her, waiting, watching, snuffing.

Later, when even the hay slept
and the shaft of the Plough pointed south,
the foal was born. Hours the mare
spent licking the foal with its glue-blind eyes.

And the foal slept by her side,
a heap of feathers ripped from a bed.
Straw never spread as soft as this.
Milk or snow never slept like a foal.

Dawn bounced up in a bright red hat,
waved at the world and skipped away.
Up staggered the foal,
its hooves were jelly-knots of foam.
Then day sniffed with its blue nose
through the open stable window, and found them –
the foal nuzzling its mother,
velvet fumbling for her milk.

Then all the trees were talking at once,
chickens scrabbled in the yard,
like golden flowers
envy withered the last stars.

Ferenc Juhász
from the Hungarian,
translated by David Wevill

24

Sheep-dreams

for Jonathan Rees

Beneath the hill,
knocked out by sleep,
the simple sheep
are dreaming still
of what they know –
the sunset glowing
on the sheaves' fists;
a rabbit listening
to silence at nightfall;
the steady lights
of moons gaining,
waxing, waning.
In sheep-dreams, sweetness
lasts and lasts –
all worlds blessed
with the same deep grass.

Lawrence Sail

Owl on the Nursery Window Sill

The owl stared hard. It gave no answers.
My mother had been gone for days.
I faced the owl; it only stared
and blinked. Nanny said we'd see
our mummy soon. I told my sister
she was coming back. I feared
the owl might fly away.
But it only blinked and blinked.

Then Nanny said we could draw it
if we liked. She got us down white paper
and some pens. My sister cried
for she was only three. She drew the owl
in crisscross lines of red. My owl was brown
with a ring around each eye.

The hard wind crashed and whined
against the glass, rattling panes
so we could scarcely hear. I wanted
our quiet owl to stay. Nanny said
we could give the pictures to our mum.
I told my sister she would be back soon.
When I looked again, the owl had flown.

Katherine Gallagher

Tree-Planting
for Julien

Five-year-olds plant an oak,
press the roots firm, their gift.
Late-autumn cold chills, distracts
but they fight back
with cheers and hugs
down their conga line.

They are making a pact
for all the trees of their lives:
chosen forests,
trees they will draw and colour,
fill with birds and flaring-golds
– that they will climb

stand under in the rain
and be hidden by,
that they will keep
to gird rainforests:
mantled, drenched in a lattice
of undergrowth and light.

Katherine Gallagher

from *Fourteen Ways of Touching the Peter*

You can push
your thumb
in the
ridge
between his
shoulder-blades
to please him.

Starting
at its root,
you can let
his whole
tail
flow
through your hand.

In hot
weather
you can itch
the fur
under
his chin. He
likes that.

Pressing
his head against
your cheek,
you can carry
him
in the dark,
safely.

In late autumn
you can find
seeds
adhering
to his fur.
There are
plenty.

Dumping
hot fish
on his plate, you can
fend
him off,
pushing
and purring.

You can have
him shrimp
along you,
breathing,
whenever
you want
to compose poems.

George MacBeth

Lizards

They emerge as arms of sun
Prise the clouds apart and stroke
The waiting, weathered wall.

Heads like probing fingertips,
Out to greet the hands that woke
Them with their golden call.

Speckled pocket dinosaurs
Dart at blink-speed from their cracks,
To stretch on smiling stones.

Summer's gift, their kiss of life,
Bathes their mottled leather backs
And lubricates their bones.

Nothing tempts their tails to twitch,
Nothing turns their polished eyes
Or troubles them, it seems.

Danger breathes her whispered call.
Stealthy wing-beats stir the skies.
They disappear like dreams.

Darren Stanley

The Mystery of the Ant

The door was locked
so no one could get in
but somehow, over the table,
an ant came crawling
with a mischievous broad grin.

With a mischievous broad grin
the ant crawled on the table
as if to say it knew
of secret passages
that he could scramble through.

But if he could scramble through
the place was insecure and open to any bug.

No wonder he looked smug.

George Szirtes

The Bee's Knees

Great hairy knees bees have as they squat
in the flowers then push off with a spring,
all six knees pumping and shoving.
With so much power they're soon airborne, resilient,
muscular, adrift.

The bee's knees.

Brilliant.

George Szirtes

My Mother Saw a Dancing Bear

My mother saw a dancing bear
By the schoolyard, a day in June.
The keeper stood with chain and bar
And whistle-pipe, and played a tune.

And bruin lifted up its head
And lifted up its dusty feet,
And all the children laughed to see
It caper in the summer heat.

They watched as for the Queen it died.
They watched it march. They watched it halt.
They heard the keeper as he cried,
'Now, roly-poly!' 'Somersault!'

And then, my mother said, there came
The keeper with a begging-cup,
The bear with burning coat of fur,
Shaming the laughter to a stop.

They paid a penny for the dance,
But what they saw was not the show;
Only, in bruin's aching eyes,
Far-distant forests, and the snow.

Charles Causley

34

The Green Bear

I am a green bear.

I do not dig a den like other bears,
Instead I build
A nest in a tree,
And climb to it at dusk,
And lie there while the mild winds
Rock me to sleep.

I am a green bear.

I do not eat berries or fish like other bears,
Instead I eat
Loaves of earth,
Which I set in the sun to dry
Until they're crunchy on the outside,
Sticky in.

I am a green bear.

I do not roar and snarl like other bears,
Instead I sing,
On moon-dark nights,
A short song
Like the foggy whistle
of a distant train.

I am a green bear.

I am the colour of grass,
if I lay down in a field
You could walk
Straight by,
And not even know I was there.
It happens often.

I am a green bear.

I have green fur and a green
Heart and green
Meat on green
Bones, and I ask myself this question:
Am I the last in a long line of green bears,
Or am I, perhaps, the first?

I am a green bear.

Richard Edwards

36

There Isn't a Monkey in the Attic

Oh, yes, there is . . .

It wakes at nightfall.
It dances across the rafters.
It swings through the roofbeams, showing its teeth.

There isn't a monkey in the attic.

Oh, yes there is.
It hunts and feasts on spiders.
It drinks from the water-tank, lapping like a cat.
It pokes a finger through the roof insulation and
    scratches on the ceiling, pretending to be a ghost.

There isn't a monkey in the attic.

Oh, yes, there is.
It opens the box of comics and leafs through them.
It unclicks the suitcase of old photographs and has
    a good laugh.
It empties the trunk of Christmas decorations and
    dresses up in them, tinsel round its shoulders, a
    fairy on top of its head.

There isn't a monkey in the attic.

Oh, yes, there is.

It sleeps in a nest of newspapers, under a dustsheet.
If you go up very quietly, you can hear its monkey
    snores,
You can smell its monkey smell.

There isn't a monkey in the attic.

Oh, yes, there is . . .

Richard Edwards

For Francesca

it's so early in the morning

the cobweb
stretched between the gateposts
is not yet broken

couples
stir in their beds
and sigh and smile
and the hard
words of the day
are not yet spoken

it's so early in the morning

the street lamps go out
one by one
the small stars disappear
and your life
has barely begun

it's so early in the morning

Helen Dunmore

Small Dawn Song

This is just to say Thank You

to the tick
  of the downstairs clock
    like a blind man's stick
      tap-tip on through the dark

to the lone
  silly blackbird who sang
    before dawn when no one
      should have been listening

to the wheeze
  and chink of the milk float
    like an old nightwatchman clinking keys
      and clearing his throat

Six o'clock and all's well
Six o'clock and all's well

The night's been going on
        so long
        so long
This is just to say Thank You.

Philip Gross

Snowy Benches

Do parks get lonely
in winter, perhaps,
when benches have only
snow on their laps?

Aileen Fisher

My Brother

I used to think
how good it would be
if I was the onliest
kid in this house.
But when you went to camp,
I was the loneliest.

Bobbi Katz

Leave Me Alone

Loving care!
Too much to bear.
Leave me alone!

      Don't brush my hair,
      Don't pat my head,
      Don't tuck me in
      Tonight in bed,
      Don't ask me if I want a sweet,
      Don't fix my favourite things to eat,
      Don't give me lots of good advice,
      And most of all just don't be nice.

But when I've wallowed well in sorrow,
Be nice to me again tomorrow.

Felice Holman

Alone on the Playground

Alone on the playground.
The foggy day is still.
I stand here like a statue
and feel an icy chill.
Houses, trees have vanished
in mist that's thick and white.
I wait alone, in silence.
There's no one else in sight.
The school door stands half open,
half scared I step inside.
The corridor lies empty,
one window's open wide.
How my footsteps echo
as I walk to the Hall.
There's music playing faintly
. . . but no one's there at all.
I walk on to my classroom,
push back the squeaky door,
see chalkmarks on the blackboard
and books upon the floor.
The building seems deserted,
but why? I've not a clue.
I think of Flannan Isle
and don't know what to do.
For sure, it's not the weekend.
It's not the half-term break.
Alone in the empty school
I shiver and I shake.
Time to get out of here,
so I head for the door,

and find the fog is swirling
much thicker than before.
Alone on the playground,
the foggy day is still
and I stand like a statue
and feel an icy chill,
and feel an icy chill . . .

Wes Magee

Where Nobody Lives

I live in the house
where nobody lives

Where the doors never open
where nobody speaks

I live in the house
in the long empty street

Where windows hang open
and broken stairs creak

I live in the house
where the dream children play

We dance through the rooms
till the moon rides away

And I sit by myself
through the slow waiting day

When no one comes here
and nobody speaks

In the house in the street
where nobody lives

Dave Ward

The Window's Eyes

The window's eyes are glazed with constant staring.
Sometimes, the sky is all too bright,
the sun beyond bearing,
at other times the dark that comes at night
seems stuck there and it's getting very late
but you lie awake and wait
for all the stars to creep
across your half-closed lids and sleep,

while the glass eyes of the houses all look out
reflecting on the streetlights, full of doubt.

George Szirtes

Give Me Back My Rags

Just come to my mind
And my thoughts will scratch out your face

Just come into my sight
And my eyes will start snarling at you

Just open your mouth
And my silence will smash your jaws

Just remind me of you
And my remembering will paw up the ground under
your feet

That's what it's come to between us

Vasko Popa
Yugoslavian poem translated from
the Serbo-Croatian by Anne Pennington

The Bully Asleep

One afternoon, when grassy
Scents through the classroom crept,
Bill Craddock laid his head
Down on his desk, and slept.

The children came round him:
Jimmy, Roger, and Jane;
They lifted his head timidly
And let it sink again.

'Look, he's gone sound asleep, Miss,'
Said Jimmy Adair;
'He stays up all night, you see;
His mother doesn't care.'

'Stand away from him, children.'
Miss Andrews stooped to see.
'Yes, he's asleep; go on
With your writing, and let him be.'

'Now's a good chance!' whispered Jimmy;
And he snatched Bill's pen and hit it.
'Kick him under the desk, hard;
He won't know who did it.'

'Fill all his pockets with rubbish –
Paper, apple-cores, chalk.'
So they plotted, while Jane
Sat wide-eyed at their talk.

Not caring, not hearing,
Bill Craddock he slept on;
Lips parted, eyes closed –
Their cruelty gone.

'Stick him with pins!' muttered Roger.
'Ink down his neck!' said Jim.
But Jane, tearful and foolish,
Wanted to comfort him.

John Walsh

The Guide

'How strange to meet you on this moor . . .
But you are lost. Here, take my hand.'
The hand was colder than a knife;
I held it though, for dear, dear life,
 For dear, dear life,
And on we walked through that weird land,
Myself behind, my guide before.

I followed on behind my guide.
Her clothes gave off an eerie glow.
'Who are you? *What* are you?' I said.
'I'm what I am,' she turned her head,
 She turned her head.
'Ask me no questions, for I know
Nothing, not even how I died.'

She never spoke another word;
And so we walked all through the night,
Past twisted tree and lumpen stone
Till the sun rose, and all alone,
 And all alone,
I found myself, bathed in the light
And sung to by the dawning bird.

And I was safe, as heaven knows.
But who my strange companion was,
What wistful ghost had held my hand,
To guide me through that unknown land,
   That nightmare land,
I never, ever learned, because
She vanished as the bright sun rose.

Gerard Benson

Witches' Chant
(from *Macbeth*)

Round about the cauldron go:
In the poisoned entrails throw.
Toad, that under cold stone
Days and nights has thirty-one
Sweated venom sleeping got,
Boil thou first in the charmed pot.
  Double, double toil and trouble;
  Fire burn and cauldron bubble.

Fillet of a fenny snake,
In the cauldron boil and bake;
Eye of newt and toe of frog,
Wool of bat and tongue of dog,
Adder's fork and blindworm's sting,
Lizard's leg and owlet's wing.
For a charm of powerful trouble,
Like a hell-broth boil and bubble.
  Double, double toil and trouble;
  Fire burn and cauldron bubble.

Scale of dragon, tooth of wolf,
Witch's mummy, maw and gulf
Of the ravenous salt-sea shark,
Root of hemlock digged in the dark,
Make the gruel thick and slab:
Add thereto a tiger's chaudron,
For the ingredients of our cauldron.
            Double, double toil and trouble;
            Fire burn and cauldron bubble.

William Shakespeare

Stufferation

Lovers lie around in it
Broken glass is found in it
Grass
I like that stuff

Tuna fish get trapped in it
Legs come wrapped in it
Nylon
I like that stuff

Eskimos and tramps chew it
Madame Tussaud gave status to it
Wax
I like that stuff

Elephants get sprayed with it
Scotch is made with it
Water
I like that stuff

Clergy are dumbfounded by it
Bones are surrounded by it
Flesh
I like that stuff

Harps are strung with it
Mattresses are sprung with it
Wire
I like that stuff

Carpenters make cots with it
Undertakers use lots of it
Wood
I like that stuff

Dirty cigarettes are lit with it
Pensioners get happy when they sit by it
Fire
I like that stuff

Johnny Dankworth's alto is made of it, most of it*
Scoobdidoo is composed of it**
Plastic
I like that stuff

Elvis kept it in his left-hand pocket
Little Richard made it zoom like a rocket
Rock 'n' Roll
Ooh my soul
I like that stuff

Apemen take it to make them hairier
I ate a ton of it in Bulgaria
Yoghurt
I like that stuff

Man-made fibres and raw materials
Old rolled gold and breakfast cereals
Platinum linoleum
I like that stuff

Skin on my hands
Hair on my head
Toenails on my feet
And linen on the bed

Well, I like that stuff
Yes
I like that stuff
The earth
Is made of earth
And I like that stuff

Adrian Mitchell

*Jazz musician John Dankworth used to play a plastic saxophone.

**Scoobdidoo was a fistful of kind of multi-coloured pieces of plastic which were a playground craze in the 1950s. It was a sad sort of toy, nothing like the exciting Hula Hoop of the same period.

Cock-A-Roodle Dock

'Cock-a-roodle dock,
My lock,
Cock-a-roodle dock.'

And the grey hand shimmered
In the shifting fog

'Cock-a-roodle dock,
My lock,
Cock-a-roodle dock.'

Till the raindrops clattered
And the lightning struck.

'Cock-a-roodle dock,
My lock,
Cock-a-roodle dock.'

Seven winds willow
In the whispering stream

'Cock-a-roodle dock,
My lock,
Cock-a-roodle dock.'

While pennywinkles curdle
The wicker child's dream.

'Cock-a-roodle dock,
My lock,
Cock-a-roodle dock.'

Where do they fly
With their petticoats high?

'Cock-a-roodle dock,
My lock,
Cock-a-roodle dock.'

Come to me, come to me,
By and by.

David Greygoose

Once Upon a Time Machine

Once upon a time machine
I woke up screaming, in a dream:
The strawberry jam had turned bright green,
The king and queen were wearing jeans,
And all the flowers ate ice cream;
Once upon a time machine.

Once upon a time machine
I wondered what it was I'd seen:
A pillow filled with pink baked beans,
A snowman made of margarine,
And a robot in a football team;
Once upon a time machine.

Once upon a time machine
I asked myself what did it mean:
On a walking, talking TV screen,
A saucepan swimming in a stream,
A sun-dial stone which struck thirteen,
And cold mince pies at Hallow'en;
Once upon a time machine.

Dave Ward

Jabberwocky

'Twas brillig, and the slithy toves
Did gyre and gimble in the wabe;
All mimsy the borogroves,
And the mome raths outgrabe.

'Beware the Jabberwock, my son!
The jaws that bite, the claws that catch!
Beware the Jubjub bird, and shun
The frumious Bandersnatch!'

He took his vorpal sword in hand:
Long time the manxome foe he sought –
So rested he by the Tumtum tree,
And stood awhile in thought.

And, as in uffish thought he stood,
The Jabberwock, with eyes of flame,
Came whiffling through the tulgy wood,
And burbled as it came!

One, two! One, two! And through and through
The vorpal blade went snicker-snack!
He left it dead, and with its head
He went galumphing back.

'And has thou slain the Jabberwock?
Come to my arms, my beamish boy!
O frabjous day! Callooh! Callay!'
He chortled in his joy.

'Twas brillig, and the slithy toves
Did gyre and gimble in the wabe:
All mimsy were the borogroves,
And the mome raths outgrabe.

Lewis Carroll

*Shoem

Time flizzes when I'm wrizzing –
some words are toomely long,
and so I merge and jummix
to squeet them in my song.

It's really not too diffcky
to get my words to scrush –
saves tromoil and timassle,
when in a hurrid rush.

There's only one small difflem
for my puzzizzy head –
I'm baffplussed and conboozled
by what it is I said!

Liz Brownlee

*Short Poem
Flizzes = flies and whizzes
Wrizzing = busy and writing
Toomely = too and extremely
Jummix = jumble and mix
Squeet = squeeze and fit
Diffcky = difficult and tricky
Scrush = squash and crush
Tromoil = trouble and turmoil
Timassle = time and hassle
Hurrid = hurried and horrid
Difflem = difficulty and problem
Puzzizzy = puzzled and dizzy
Baffplussed = baffled and nonplussed
Conboozled = confused and bamboozled

Unscrambled Egg

Humpty Dumpty's famous
for his terrifying fall:
Obviously ovoids
don't belong upon a wall!

They called the army out at once;
the King enjoyed the joke:
He lined up all his soldiers
and he dipped them in the yolk!

Tony Charles

A Bad Princess

A bad princess stomped through the woods
in a pair of boots
        looking for trouble –
diamond tiara, satin dress, hair an absolute mess,
ready to bubble.

Imagine her shock and surprise
when she bumped straight into
        her very own double:

a Tree Girl,
with shiny holly-green eyes
and a crown of autumn leaves on her wild head,
the colour of both of their hair.

Don't you dare, screamed Bad,
walk in these Royal woods looking like me!

I shall do as I please, you grumpy old thing,
said Tree.
Give me those emeralds that hang from your ears
or I'll kick you hard
and pinch you meanly.
Then we'll see which one of we two
is cut out
    to be Queenly!

Oh! The bad Princess turned
                    and ran,
ran for her life
into the arms of the dull young Prince
and became his wife.

Carol Ann Duffy

Three

I met a miniature King
by the side of the road,
wearing a crown
and an ermine suit –
important, small,
plump as a natterjack toad.
Kneel! he shrieked, *Kneel for the King!*
Certainly not, I said,
I'll do no such thing.

I saw a Giantess,
tall as a tree.
You'll do for a doll, she bellowed,
just the toy for me!
Into the box! Scream hard! Scream long!
I stared at her mad pond eyes
then skipped away.
Dream on . . .

I bumped into an Invisible Boy – *ouch!* –
at the edge of the field.
Give me a chocolate drop
said a voice.
What do you say? said I.
Please.
So I did
then stared as it floated mid-air
and melted away.

These are three of the people I met yesterday.

Carol Ann Duffy

Extracts from *The Tempest*

'Caliban's complaint' (Act 1, Scene 2)

> This island's mine, by Sycorax my mother,
> Which thou tak'st from me. When thou cam'st
> first,
> Thou strok'st me and made much of me, would'st
> give me
> Water with berries in't, and teach me how
> To name the bigger light, and how the less,
> That burn by day and night; and then I lov'd
> thee.
> And show'd thee all the qualities o' th' isle,
> The fresh springs, brine-pits, barren place and
> fertile.
> Curs'd be I that did so. All the charms
> Of Sycorax, toads, beetles, bats, light on you!
> For I am all the subjects that you have,
> Which first was mine own king; and here you sty
> me
> In this hard rock, whiles you keep from me
> The rest o' th' island.

'Full fathom five' (Act 1, Scene 2)

> Full fathom five thy father lies;
> Of his bones are coral made;
> Those are pearls that were his eyes;
> Nothing of him that doth fade,
> But doth suffer a sea change
> Into something rich and strange.
> Sea-nymphs hourly ring his knell:
> Ding-dong,
> Hark now I hear them, ding-dong bell.

'Caliban speaks of the isle' (Act 3, Scene 2)

> Be not afeard. The isle is full of noises,
> Sounds and sweet airs that give delight and hurt
>   not.
> Sometimes a thousand twangling instruments
> Will hum about mine ears; and sometimes voices,
> That, if I then had wak'd after long sleep,
> Will make me sleep again; and then, in dreaming,
> The clouds methought would open and show
>   riches
> Ready to drop upon me, that, when I wak'd,
> I cried to dream again.

'Where the bee sucks' (Act 5, Scene 1)

> Where the bee sucks, there suck I;
> In a cowslip's bell I lie;
> There I couch when owls do cry.
> On the bat's back I do fly
> After summer merrily.
> Merrily, merrily shall I live now
> Under the blossom that hangs on the bough.

William Shakespeare

Wolf in My Pocket

The wolf in my pocket is hungry
because he can't watch the moon,
because the winter snow has melted without him,
because the stitching of the sun
on pine tree shadow
is far away and unforgotten,

the wolf in my pocket is angry,
beating a path where the zip
rasps but never opens,
he lollops up and down the lining
catching fluffballs in his claws –
his grey fur is too warm,

the wolf in my pocket howls
as he turns by the seam,
once he had cubs and a cave for them,
now he has none,
once he was cold and alive
on dangerous nights
but now he sleeps and his tongue
hangs out for nothing.

Helen Dunmore

It's Dark in Here

I am writing these lines
From inside a lion,
And it's rather dark in here.
So please excuse the handwriting
Which may not be too clear.
But this afternoon by the lion's cage
I'm afraid I got too near.
And I'm writing these lines
From inside a lion,
And it's rather dark in here.

Shel Silverstein

This is Just to Say

I have eaten
the plums
that were in
the icebox
and which
you were probably
saving for breakfast

Forgive me
they were delicious
so sweet
and so cold

William Carlos Williams

Variations on a Theme

1.

I chopped down the house that you had been saving to
   live in next summer.
I am sorry, but it was morning, and I had nothing to do
and its wooden beams were so inviting.

2.

We laughed at the hollyhocks together
and then I sprayed them with lye.
Forgive me. I simply do not know what I am doing.

3.

I gave away the money that you had been saving to live
   on for the next ten years.
The man who asked for it was shabby
and the firm March wind on the porch was so juicy and
   cold.

4.

Last evening we went dancing and I broke your leg.
Forgive me. I was clumsy, and
I wanted you here in the wards, where I am the doctor.

Kenneth Koch

Clementine

In a cavern, in a canyon,
   Excavating for a mine
Lived a miner, forty-niner,
   And his daughter, Clementine.

Oh, my darling, oh, my darling,
   Oh, my darling Clementine,
You are lost and gone forever,
   Dreadful sorry, Clementine.

Anonymous
(American popular song)

In a cavern, in a canyon

In a cavern, in a canyon
  Lay an unexpected mine.
Don't know where, Dear. DO TAKE CARE, DEAR . . .
  Dreadful sorry, Clementine.

Paul Dehn

Sing a Song of Sixpence

Sing a song of sixpence,
A pocket full of rye,
Four and twenty blackbirds
Baked in a pie.

When the pie was opened
The birds began to sing –
Wasn't that a dainty dish
To set before the king?

The king was in the counting-house
Counting out his money,
The queen was in the parlour
Eating bread and honey.

The maid was in the garden
Hanging out the clothes.
When down flew a blackbird
And pecked off her nose.

Anonymous

Sing a Song of Subways

Sing a song of subways,
Never see the sun;
Four-and-twenty people
In room for one.

When the doors are opened –
Everybody run.

Eve Merriam

Instructions for Giants

Please do not step on swing parks, youth clubs,
      cinemas or discos.
Please flatten all schools!

Please do not eat children, pop stars, TV soap actors,
      kind grannies who give us 50p.
Please feel free to gobble up dentists and teachers
      any time you like!

Please do not block out the sunshine.
Please push all rain clouds over to France.

Please do not drink the public swimming pool.
Please eat all cabbage fields, vegetable plots
and anything green that grows in the
      boring countryside!

Please do not trample kittens, lambs or other baby
      animals.
Please take spiders and snakes, ants and beetles home
      for your own pets.

Please stand clear of jets passing.
Please sew up the ozone layer.
Please mind where you're putting your big feet –
And no sneaking off to China when we're playing
      hide-and-seek!

John Rice

The Sleepy Giant

My age is three hundred and seventy-two,
And I think with the deepest regret,
How I used to pick up and voraciously chew
The dear little boys whom I met.

I've eaten them raw, in their holiday suits;
I've eaten them curried with rice;
I've eaten them baked, in their jackets and boots,
And found them exceedingly nice.

But now that my jaws are weak for such fare,
I think it exceedingly rude
To do such a thing, when I'm quite well aware
Little boys do not like to be chewed.

And so I contentedly live upon eels,
And try to do nothing amiss,
And I pass all the time I can spare from my meals
In innocent slumber – like this.

Charles Edward Carryl

One of the Difficulties of Writing a Poem

On to the world's shoulders
Snow falls like dandruff

Snow falls like dandruff
On to the world's shoulders

Like dandruff, snow
Falls on to the world's shoulders

Snow, like dandruff, falls
On to the world's shoulders

On to the world's shoulders
Like dandruff, snow falls

Dandruff like snow
Falls on to the world's shoulders

On to the world's shoulders
Dandruff falls like snow.

Brian Patten

The Computer's First Christmas Card

jollymerry
hollyberry
jollyberry
merryholly
happyjolly
jollyjelly
jellybelly
bellymerry
hollyheppy
jollyMolly
marryJerry
merryHarry
hoppyBarry
jeppyJarry
boppyheppy
berryjorry
jorryjolly
moppyjelly
Mollymerry
Jerryjolly
bellyboppy
jorryhoppy
hollymoppy
Barrymerry
Jarryhappy
happyboppy
boppyjolly
jollymerry
merrymerry
merrymerry

83

merryChris
ammerryasa
Chrismerry
asMERRYCHR
YSANTHEMUM

Edwin Morgan

Snake

Sneaky Mr.
Forked tongue Twr.
Caught my Sr.
When he Kr.
Gave her a Blr.

Valerie Bloom

A Fistful of Pacifists

A thimbleful of giants
A rugby scrum of nuns
An atom of elephants
A cuddle of guns

A rustle of rhinoceros
A barrel of bears
A swear box of politicians
A bald patch of hairs

A stumble of ballet dancers
A flutter of whales
A mouthful of silence
A whisper of gales

A pocketful of earthquakes
A conference of pears
A fistful of pacifists
A round-up of squares

David Kitchen

Kennings Cat

Tail-flicker
Fur-licker
Tree-scratcher
Mouse-catcher
Basket-sleeper
Night-creeper
Eye-blinker
Milk-drinker
Lap-sitter
Ball-hitter
Fish-eater
Fire-heater
String-muddler
Kitten-cuddler
Angry-hisser
Wet-kisser
Wall-prowler
Moon-howler
Cream-lapper
Claw-tapper
Cat-flapper

Sandy Brownjohn

Winter Haikus

This cold day's sharp frost
Seems to hold an icy knife
At the shy Sun's throat.

'Our winter draws on,'
My grandmother used to say.
But why did she smile?

New ice sheets the street.
Old men shuffle with great care,
And cling to their wives.

Wind in the chimney;
Slates slide from the winter roof.
We lie safe in bed.

Winter seems so long
When you become old and grey
Beside a small fire.

John Kitching

The Limerick Orchestra

If you rant and you rave and you bellow,
Then listen a while to the cello.
With the sweetest of strings
This fine cello sings.
It will make you a more mellow fellow.

Her fingers just stroking the keys,
She plays the piano with ease.
Rock and roll, jazz or blues,
Any classics you choose,
Her playing is certain to please.

With her lightning fingers and thumbs,
She's magic with cymbals and drums.
She adds to her tricks
With brushes and sticks,
Manufacturing rhythmical plums.

A man in an elegant suit
Plays a flirtatious tune on his flute.
Helped by fleetest of fingers,
The melody lingers.
This flautist is really astute.

John Kitching

Palindrome

It gets you back
To where you began
You simply run on
The same way you ran

Though you'll never restart
Where you first had begun
And no return
Is ever square one

But do not stop
To think of home
At the halfway point
Of a palindrome

For that's where the mirror
Cracks in two
There is no way back
And no way through

Lawrence Sail

Riddle

My constant companion,
he's a nose-poker

and gat-toothed.
He prevents my entrances.

I must get hold of him,
show him where I need him,

push and pull him.
Then I'm home and dry.

Kevin Crossley-Holland

Riddles

I

I am at your beginning and your end.
I dog your footsteps
And cannot be shaken off.
Though I fade from view
You are never alone.
So silent that you often forget me.
I am still there,
Your constant dark spy and companion.

II

My slender figure charms
dressed in white or bright colours.
The frills of my dress grow and gather
As I grow smaller
Lighting your celebratory tree
A comfort in the darkness,
A small welcoming warmth.

John Cotton

Old English Riddle

A moth, I thought, munching a word.
How marvellously weird! a worm
Digesting a man's sayings –
A sneakthief nibbling in the shadows
At the shape of a poet's thunderous phrases –
How unutterably strange!
And the pilfering parasite none the wiser
For the words he has swallowed.

from The Exeter Book
translated by Gerard Benson

Goodnight

The click of a switch.

In his glass bowl the gold snake

is at once asleep.

Pamela Gillilan

Frostbringer

Look pal, I wear my hat like this for a reason.
If I straighten it, you know what happens?
The world freezes. I mean rigid;
birds in flight suddenly solid,
falling onto smashed ponds. Tilt
this tifter and the whole earth spills
from its axis, winter sweeps in. I can
do that. Call it a gift.

        And then
rivers set instantly, waterfalls in mid crash,
out of the taps only a drip that freezes.
Solid ice stoppers will rise from milk bottles
and kiddies will cry and everyone's heart
go hard. Beggars will be ignored
and no one give to charity, concert halls
and churches cold as graves. Brother, If I
wanted I could close down every motorway
and every airport and seal the planet
in a swirling net of white. Old men
would drop dead and foxes come to farms
and everyone be trapped in their own doors,
cities would starve and governments fall
and no one would love his neighbour at all
because my snow would be head high
and blanketing the kingdom.

So I
keep the jaunty angle. By such small
mercies, these few degrees, do we survive.

Catherine Fisher

The Apple-Raid

Darkness came early, though not yet cold;
Stars were strung on the telegraph wires;
Street lamps spilled pools of liquid gold;
The breeze was spiced with garden fires.

That smell of burnt leaves, the early dark,
Can still excite me but not as it did
So long ago when we met in the park -
Myself, John Peters and David Kidd.

We moved out of town to the district where
The lucky and wealthy had their homes
With garages, gardens, and apples to spare
Ripely clustered in the trees' green domes.

We chose the place we meant to plunder
And climbed the wall and dropped down to
The secret dark. Apples crunched under
Our feet as we moved through the grass and dew.

The clusters on the lower boughs of the tree
Were easy to reach. We stored the fruit
In pockets and jerseys until all three
Boys were heavy with their tasty loot.

Safe on the other side of the wall
We moved back to town and munched as we went.
I wonder if David remembers at all
That little adventure, the apples' fresh scent.

Stange to think that he's fifty years old,
That tough little boy with scabs on his knees;
Stranger to think that John Peters lies cold
In an orchard in France beneath apple trees.

Vernon Scannell

Acknowledgements

The publishers wish to thank the following for permission to use copyright materials:

Gerard Benson: 'The Guide', 'Old English Riddle' (first published as a poster by *Poems on the Underground*), by permission of the author. **Valerie Bloom:** 'Snake', from *The World is Sweet*, Bloomsbury Children's Books (2000) by permission of the author. **Sandy Brownjohn:** 'Kennings Cat', from *Both Sides of the Catflap*, Hodder Children's Books, (1996) by permission of the author. **Liz Brownlee:** 'Shoem', by permission of the author. **Charles Edward Carryl:** 'The Sleepy Giant', from *Poems for 10 year olds*, ed. Susie Gibbs, Macmillan Children's Books, (2000). **Charles Causley:** 'My Mother Saw a Dancing Bear', from *Selected Poems*, Macmillan, by permission of David Higham Associates on behalf of the author. **Tony Charles:** 'Unscrambled Egg', by permission of the author. **Pie Corbett:** 'Take Two', 'Goodnight Stroud', by permission of the author, 'City Jungle' from *Rice, Pie and Moses*, Macmillan (1995) by permission of the author. **John Cotton:** 'Riddles', by permission of the author. **Kevin Crossley-Holland:** 'Riddle' by permission of the author. **Paul Dehn:** 'In a Cavern' is reprinted with permission of Simon and Schuster from *Quake, Quake, Quake* by Paul Dehn. Copyright © 1958, 1961 by Paul Dehn. **Carol Ann Duffy:** 'The Oldest Girl in the World', 'A Bad Princess', 'Three' from *The Oldest Girl in the World*, (2001) by permission of Faber and Faber Ltd. **Helen Dunmore:** 'Hedgehog Hiding at Harvest in Hills Above Monmouth', 'For Francesca', 'Wolf in My Pocket', by permission of Scholastic Ltd, from Snollygoster © Helen Dunmore 2001, 'Pomegranites Do Not Feel Pain' from Secrets, Bodley Head, by permission of A. P. Watt Ltd on behalf of the author. **Richard Edwards:** 'The Green Bear', 'There isn't a monkey in the attic', by permission of the author, **Aileen Fisher:** 'Snowy Benches', from Out in the Dark and Daylight. Copyright©1980 by Aileen Fisher. Used by permission of Marian Reiner for the author. **Catherine Fisher:** 'Frostbringer', by permission of the author. **Katherine Gallagher:** 'Owl on the Nursery Sill', by permission of the author. 'Tree Planting' from *Fish-rings on Water* (Forest Books 1989) by permission of the author. **Pamela Gillilan:** 'Goodnight', by permission of the author. **Philip Gross:** 'Small Dawn Song', from *The All-Nite Café* (1993) by permission of Faber and Faber Ltd. **Felice Holman:** 'Leave me alone' from At the Top of My Voice and Other Poems, by Felice Holman. Charles Scribner's Sons,©1970. Reprinted by permission of Felice Holman, copyright owner. **Ted Hughes:** 'New Year Exhileration', from Moortown Diary by Ted Hughes, by permission of Faber and Faber Ltd. **Ferenc Juhász:** 'The Birth of a Foal', Penguin Books Ltd and Mr David Wevill for his translation of 'Birth of the Foal'. **Bobbi Katz:** 'My Brother', copyright©1991 from *Could We Be Friends*, Poems for Pals, by Bobbi Katz. Reprinted with permission of the author. **David Kitchen:** 'A Fistful of Pacifists', from *Never Play Leapfrog with a Unicorn*, published by William Heinemann (a division of Reed International) 1995. **John Kitching:** 'Winter Haikus', 'The Limerick Orchestra' by permission of the author. **Kenneth Koch:** 'Variations on a Theme' by William Carlos Williams', from *Thank you and other poems*. Reprinted by permission of the author. **George MacBeth:** '*from* Fourteen Ways of touching the Peter', from *Collected Poems 1958-1982*, Hutchinson. **Wes Magee:** 'Alone on the Playground', by

99

Ramshackle Rainbow

Ramshackle Rainbow is a dazzling collection of poems that you will want to turn to again and again from poets as varied as Helen Dunmore, Brian Patten and Lewis Caroll by way of William Carlos Williams and Charles Causley. The poems reflect the national literacy strategy for Year 5.

Heatwave

Heat over all; a lark can rise
Into the arching sun;
The moor like a lion sleeping lies –
Rough mane on burning stone.
Not a harebell shakes; the wild blue flags
Of wind are folded up.
Here on the hill the air is still
As water in a cup.

Phoebe Hesketh

A selected list of poetry books available from Macmillan

The prices shown below are correct at the time of going to press. However, Macmillan Publishers reserve the right to show new retail prices on covers which may differ from those previously advertised.

The Snake Hotel	0 330 48261 0
Slithering poems, chosen by Brian Moses	£3.50
The Penguin in the Fridge	0 330 48019 7
Poems by Peter Dixon	£3.50
Superheroes	0 330 48262 9
Fearless poems, chosen by Paul Cookson	£2.99
Tongue Twisters and Tonsil Twizzlers	0 330 34941 4
Poems chosen by Paul Cookson	£2.99
Let's Twist Again	0 330 37559 8
More tongue twisters chosen by Paul Cookson	£2.99
A Sea Creature Ate My Teacher	0 330 39064 3
Poems chosen by Brian Moses	£2.99
Never Stare at a Grizzly Bear	0 330 39121 6
Poems by Nick Toczek	£2.99
Teacher's Pets	0 330 36868 0
Poems chosen by Paul Cookson	£2.99

All Macmillan titles can be ordered at your local bookshop or are available by post from:

Book Service by Post
PO Box 29, Douglas, Isle of Man IM99 1BQ

Credit cards accepted. For details:
Telephone: 01624 675137
Fax: 01624 670923
E-mail: bookshop@enterprise.net

Free postage and packing in the UK.
Overseas customers: add £1 per book (paperback)
and £3 per book (hardback).